ANTARCTIC ADVENTURE

Contents

Haydn Middleton

Story illustrated by Seb Burnett

Before Reading

In this story

 Schoolboy Mo who is also Mole Man

 The Big Slug, his arch enemy

 Emperor Penguin

Tricky words

- Antarctica
- twitching
- anywhere
- ordinary
- tunnel
- oven
- massive
- icy

Introduce these tricky words and help the reader when they come across them later!

Story starter

Mo is no ordinary boy. He has a very special nose. And when he smells trouble, something amazing happens – Mo turns into a super-hero called Mole Man! One day, the class was learning about Antarctica when Mo smelled bad trouble. Could it be his arch enemy, the Big Slug?

Mole Man
at the
South Pole

Mo was sitting in class.

"Today we are going to learn about Antarctica," said his teacher.

Just then, Mo's nose started twitching.

Mo had a special nose. He could smell trouble anywhere in the world.
And he smelled **bad** trouble now.
"Can I get my pen from my bag?" asked Mo. And he ran off.

Mo rushed to his secret spot –
and he burst out of his school clothes.

Mo was not an ordinary boy any more.
Mo was now ... **Mole Man**!
"Sniff, sniff," went Mole Man.
"Time to go digging."

So Mole Man set off underground
to find the trouble.
He dug faster than the speed of light!

Mole Man dug under land and sea.
"I bet the Big Slug is behind this trouble," he said. "But Mole Man can sort it out."
Soon his nose was twitching really fast.
"Sniff, sniff," went Mole Man.
"Time to tunnel *up*."

A moment later, he burst up through the ground.

He was at the South Pole, in the middle of Antarctica!

But something was wrong.

The snow and ice were *melting*!

"Mole Man!" cried Emperor Penguin. "You've come at just the right time! We're in terrible trouble. The Big Slug has built the world's biggest pizza oven under the South Pole. It's so hot, it's making the whole of Antarctica melt!"

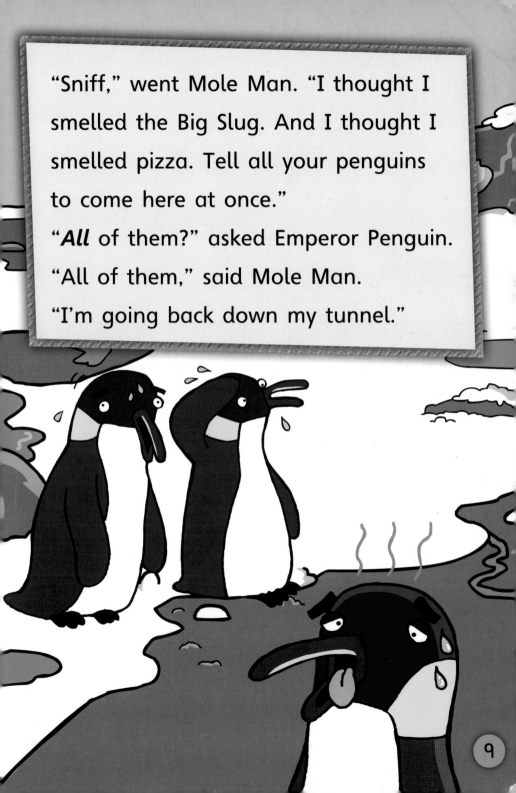

"Sniff," went Mole Man. "I thought I smelled the Big Slug. And I thought I smelled pizza. Tell all your penguins to come here at once."

"*All* of them?" asked Emperor Penguin.

"All of them," said Mole Man. "I'm going back down my tunnel."

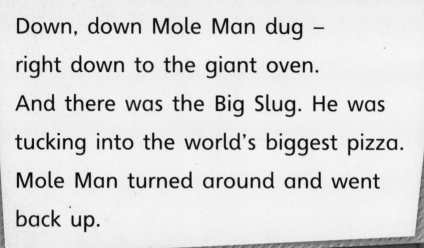

Down, down Mole Man dug –
right down to the giant oven.
And there was the Big Slug. He was
tucking into the world's biggest pizza.
Mole Man turned around and went
back up.

A massive army of penguins was
waiting.

"Excellent," said Mole Man.

"Now what should we do?"
asked Emperor Penguin.

"I want you all to take a deep breath," said Mole Man. "And when I say 'Blow!' I want you to blow down my tunnel!" All the penguins nodded.

"Ready, steady, **BLOW**!" cried Mole Man.

The penguins all blew.

Their breath made an icy wind.

The wind rushed all the way down

Mole Man's tunnel – and it froze

the pizza oven!

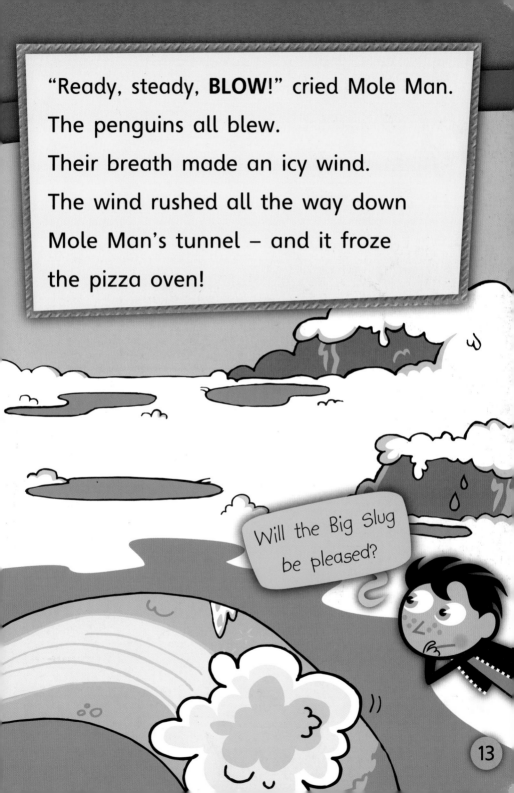

Will the Big Slug be pleased?

The Big Slug was very cross.

"Our oven has frozen!" he cried.

"We'll never get it hot again.

This must be the work of Mole Man!

I'm coming to get you, Mole Man!"

But he couldn't move –
his body had frozen too!

"Hope you like frozen pizza,"
shouted Mole Man.

Everything in Antarctica was icy cold again.

"Cool! Thank you, Mole Man," said Emperor Penguin.

"No problem!" said Mole Man.

Then he dug all the way back to school and he changed into his school clothes.

Mo rushed into class.

"Just in time," said his teacher.

"Where on Earth have you been?"

"Just to Antarctica," said Mo.

His teacher smiled.

"You and your little stories," he said.

Text Detective

- Why was Antarctica melting?
- What do you think of Mole Man's plan to stop the Big Slug?

Word Detective

- **Phonic Focus:** Doubling consonants
  Page 3: What must be added to 'sit' before adding 'ing'?
- Page 7: Find a word meaning the opposite of 'right'.
- Page 9: Why is the word 'all' in italics?

Super Speller

Read these words:

sitting   digging   biggest

Now try to spell them!

Q What did the sea say to the iceberg?

A Nothing – it just waved.

Find out about

- How Captain Scott tried to get to Antarctica, at the very bottom of the world

Tricky words

- Antarctica
- ponies
- sledges
- Roald Amundsen
- weather
- terribly
- bravely

Introduce these tricky words and help the reader when they come across them later!

Text starter

Until a hundred years ago, no one had ever been to the South Pole. Then suddenly two men decided to travel there. The race was on! Who would get there first: Captain Scott of England, or Roald Amundsen of Norway?

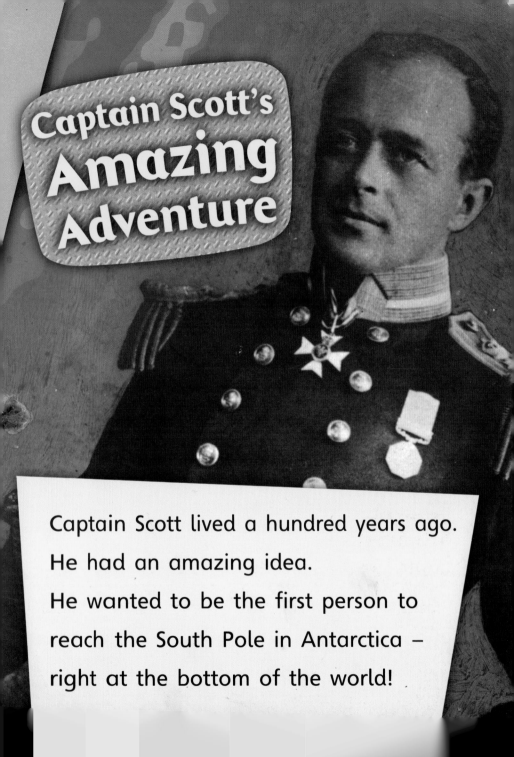

Captain Scott's Amazing Adventure

Captain Scott lived a hundred years ago.

He had an amazing idea.

He wanted to be the first person to reach the South Pole in Antarctica – right at the bottom of the world!

Captain Scott picked a team of over fifty men to help him.

He took ponies and sledges too.

They all set off for Antarctica.

On the way, Scott heard some bad news. Someone *else* had picked a team to get to the South Pole! His name was Roald Amundsen, from Norway. Now it would be a race to the Pole!

Amundsen was very good at using sledges pulled by husky dogs.

Scott's team arrived in Antarctica.
Antarctica is huge and covered in
ice and snow.
The South Pole is right in the middle.

But the weather was too bad to set off
for the South Pole, so Scott's team
built a camp on the coast.

A hundred miles along the coast,
Amundsen's team built their camp.
They could not see Scott's team,
and Scott's team could not see them.
But both teams knew they would soon
be in a race.

Scott picked just four men for the last stage of the race to the South Pole. They took some dogs and ponies with them to pull sledges. On the sledges were the food and the tents.

Scott planned to get to the South Pole in fifty days, then get back before the weather got bad again.

Scott's team walked and walked.
Sometimes they had to climb
ice mountains – in fog, winds
and snow!

It was too hard for the dogs and
ponies. Sadly, they died.
Now the five men had to pull the
sledges themselves.

On and on they walked.

Even on Christmas Day they dragged
the sledges for fifteen miles.

Were they winning?

Were they losing?

Was Amundsen's team still in the race?

At last, Scott and his team got to the South Pole.

No one had ever set foot there before.

Or had they?

Scott's men found a tent with a flag flying above it.

Amundsen's team had left it behind.

They had got to the South Pole first!

Scott and his team headed back.
But the weather was getting bad again.
Soon the team began to run out of
food. One of the men fell terribly ill
– and he died.

His name was Teddy Evans.

His name was Lawrence Oates.

Scott and the others walked on.
Then another man fell so ill,
he found it hard to walk. But he didn't
want to slow the others down.
So he bravely left the tent.
Then he let himself freeze to death.

Only three men were left.
The weather got even worse, and the
men grew too weak to keep walking.
All three died in the tent.

Eight months later, a search party
found their bodies.

Captain Scott's amazing adventure had ended very sadly.

Amundsen and his team were the winners but everyone knew Scott and his team had been very brave. They are still famous today.

Quiz

Text Detective

- Why did Captain Scott want to get to the South Pole?
- Do you think Captain Scott was brave or foolish?

Word Detective

- **Phonic Focus:** Doubling consonants
  Page 26: What must be added to 'win' before adding 'ing'?
- Page 26: Find a word which means 'pulled along'.
- Page 27: Why is the word 'they' in italics?

Super Speller

Read these words:

planned   dragged   winning

Now try to spell them!

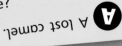

HA! HA! HA!

Q What's got two humps and lives at the South Pole?

A A lost camel.